THE PINEAPPLE B

"Every child is an artist. The problem is how to remaiɪ

ISSO

Early one Maui morning, as the sun was about ready to make her grand appearance, my two dogs and I were weaving our way down through the pineapple fields that lead to the cliff edge overlooking the North Shore. Rows and rows of neatly planted golden, glowing pineapples made me feel as if I were walking through a royal pineapple courtyard with thousands of richly attired, crown-clad pineapples. A warm, golden glow from the rising sun began to spread across the fields. The overwhelming beauty and wisdom of nature compelled me to my knees as I humbly opened my heart to the love and wisdom of nature that surrounded me.

When I opened my eyes, I had the feeling that the pineapples were smiling and reaching out with their long, green, pointy arm-like leaves, offering me a beautiful pineapple crown. This royal family was blessing me as one of their own. They seemed to be saying, "We, the pineapples, now do crown and honor you!" My entire being felt illuminated as if this imagined pineapple crown was reflecting golden rays off the sun. I felt beautiful as the warm sweet trade winds blew softly across my face. When I stood up, I felt taller, like I had magically grown another two or three feet.

Slowly and calmly, with a deep ocean of love in my heart, I continued my royal promenade down to the sea. I shared silent applauds and smiles of respect and appreciation with the pineapples. Glowing and celebrating this newfound feeling of royalty, I hadn't a worry or care in the world. Could I really be feeling this good? This beautiful? This powerful? What was happening? I was awakening to the queen in me!

Whether this was a rebirthing of my power, creativity and imagination or an actual divine inspiration, I wasn't sure, but whatever it was, I felt great and was thankful for the blessing! Could Mother Nature and my positive, creative imagination really make me feel so blessed, happy and alive? Yes to them all!

From that day on I have become known among my friends as "The Pineapple Queen." The pineapples continue to inspire me and gift me with nature loving, Spirit-infused exercises and meditations. They have shown me how to lighten up and move my "grownup" over.

I now invite you and your inner child to come out and play. REMEMBER: YOU ARE ROYALTY! I hereby offer a pineapple crown to you! Put it on and let's have fun while we create and heal ourselves and the world with our love!

Awaken Your Royalty

with
HONG-SAU YOGA

A playful blending of Body, Mind and Spirit

by
Heidi Hohani, P.T.

Credits

Author and Publisher
Heidi Hohani

Illustrator
Nichola Moss

Editors
Barbara Wood and Daryl Sroufe

Manuscript Review
Jasmyne Boswell, Jamei Tierney, Happy Oasis, Barbara Peterson, Melinda Moore,
Cathy Carr, Rosie Quigly, Chinta Mackinnon

Design and Production
Barbara Wood

© 2011 HONG-SAU YOGA   ISBN: 978-0-615-55529-4

Printed in HK

Introduction

You deserve to embody your heart's desire. It is your birthright as a Divine being. To help move your life in that direction, I share this three-part, powerfully fun process involving body, mind and spirit.

I have developed over seventy exercises and activities designed to enliven, inspire and uplift. You will set intentions and develop the omnipresent source within.

This book is not just a normal exercise book, nor is it from a formal spiritual lineage. It is a playful approach that was revealed to me while in the pineapple fields of Maui.

Hong-Sau Yoga demonstrates and calls us to a deeper truth that is emerging in this age: That we are each a source of guidance and have access to the deep wisdom within.

It has become my energizing daily practice and I hope it will become yours.

For my children
Jesse, Timothy, Matthew and Tatiana

Table of Contents

Exercises

HONG-SAU YOGA

The practice manual

Maui's own Heidi Hohani, MPQ*
*Founder and director of the HONG-SAU Research Institute
located in the pineapple fields of Maui*
*Maui Pineapple Queen

AWAKEN YOUR ROYALTY

To awaken your Royalty means to *remember* who you are! Acknowledging that you are the Divine. We are all Royalty. You are! I am! We are! This is a waking-up time for the whole world. We have been socialized to forget and believe that we are separate from the Divine. But as we commit to the process of *remembering*, we "remember" our Oneness with the Divine and with each other. This will transform us into the spirit-filled, healthy, powerful leaders we are meant to be.

It is a time in our world's history to awaken and balance our mind and body with Spirit. Calling out to all, to the old, the young and everyone in between. We are each so powerful and hold so much light. We must release and transform our feelings of fear and inadequacies if we are to let our light shine. We must do this in order to create a more loving, beautiful world.

The Mysterious yet Scientific
HONG-SAU YOGA!

YOGA is the universal science of Divine union of the soul with Spirit. The World English Dictionary defines it as: "A philosophy advocating and prescribing a course of physical and mental disciplines for attaining liberation … and union of the self with the Supreme Being or ultimate principle."

HONG-SAU (pronounced "hung-saw") is a Sanskrit chant meaning "Thee in Me, Me in Thee."

HONG-SAU YOGA is a combination of mind affirmations and body movements to bring us into union with the One Divine Spirit and bring vitality into our human body temples. Hong-Sau Yoga acknowledges Spirit as the one unifying, healing omnipresent power that can bring peace and well-being into your journey here on planet Earth.

Hong-Sau Yoga is a new and yet very ancient way of looking at and living life. When Body, Mind and Spirit work in balance and in harmony with each other, we feel light, happy and creative. When out of harmony, we feel disgruntled, frustrated and stuck. Rising stress-filled lifestyles have made us forget that we can rely on the power of Spirit to guide and inspire us in all areas of our lives. Taking time to harmonize and integrate our Body, Mind and Spirit brings "Heaven on Earth" to us, right now. Wake up sweet Royal Family of Kings and Queens! It is our Divine heritage!

HOW TO MAXIMIZE EACH EXERCISE

1. GO OUTSIDE!

Mother Nature has so much to give and teach us. Not only does being outside empower the practice, but it is also a way we can give back our love and gratitude to Her. If you are unable to do this, envision being surrounded by the beauty of nature.

2. REMEMBER

Mentally acknowledge the presence of the Divine in you and everywhere. Begin your session with a positive welcoming sentence to that greater Self, such as, "Welcome sweet Spirit in me! I love You! Thank you for this time to commune, learn, play and be guided by You today! Thank you for bringing my awareness back to You once again. I am grateful."

3. FEEL

Drop into your heart and *feel* God's presence all around. Commune with nature.

Use all your senses to confirm that life is run by Divine order, intelligence and beauty - including you! LISTEN deeply to the sounds around you. LOOK at the beautiful art displays of nature – a flower, a tree, the clouds. SMELL all the freshness of a new day. FEEL the wind. TOUCH the earth. BREATHE it all in!

4. CHOOSE AN EXERCISE AND VERBALIZE THE MANTRA

Choose one of the exercises. Memorize the movement and the mind mantra. Repeat the mind mantra out loud and/or sing it. I have heard it said that singing your prayers greatly multiplies their strength. I have experienced this and believe it to be true. Just be free and spontaneous, expressing only smiles of love, lightness and acceptance, however your voice may sound. If you need to, open the book in front of you. Feel free to change, modify or individualize the mantra and movement to best suit you and your needs. Focus on the words; feel the images of what you are saying. Train and focus your mind to stay on your intention as you say or sing the mantra. Each exercise should be performed with deep attention and intention. Send the life energy into each body part with your willpower. Underneath the exterior, fragile human body lies the power and strength of the Divine energy. By exercise, focus and devotion, we begin to tap into this forgotten source of life.

5. BREATHE AND RELAX

Inhale slowly and deeply. Exhale slowly and completely. Alternate the spoken mind mantra that is written for each exercise with silence or unspoken focus on the Divine. Our awareness of the breath is a direct connection to our Spirit.

6. PUT IT ALL TOGETHER

Follow the exercise instructions and allow your Body, Mind and Spirit to work together. As you begin using deliberate thought, mantra and physical movement, you are planting your desired intention deep into your consciousness. Trust that it is so. Repeat until your heart is content.

7. PAUSE

Take a moment to rest in gratitude.

MAKE EVERY DAY A HOLI-DAY
with
MEDITATION VACATIONS!

Although I think of my Hong-Sau exercises and walking activities as a type of "Meditation in Motion," I wanted to take a moment to emphasize the importance of "still" meditations, where one does not engage in bodily movement. When we let go of the sensation of movement we are able to drop even deeper into the stillness of the Infinite Source. Meditation also works physically with the endocrine and nervous systems to create new patterns of health.

Meditation is a vacation! And it's free! Meditation is a trip into your deeper mind, a time to get away from the busy surface mind of thought after thought. It is a time to connect with the deeper you!

For some reason many people have linked the word meditation to a practice only certain types of people do. They think it's impossible to quiet the busy mind. Continuous thoughts popping into the mind can be quite bothersome, especially once you become aware of how intruding and unruly they are! But you are much more than even your thoughts! Thoughts are our artistry tools that we use to create our lives here on Earth. They are not who we are, rather they are what we use. If we don't take a step back and observe our thoughts, like wild horses they will take us on a ride we don't necessarily want to take and bring us to places in our minds we don't necessarily want to go – stories about ourselves and others that are destructive to the well-being of ourselves and all our relations.

Meditation reminds me of scuba diving. You go into another dimension of life and the deeper you go, the more still, peaceful and alert to life you become.

I think of the Bible scripture, "Be still and know that I AM." Be present. I am here, I am now.

If you are new to meditation, below are just a few more suggestions to help get you started.

1. As you prepare to sit down and begin your meditation, remember that you are about to engage in a Divine appointment, a holy date on a "Holi-Day!" Yipee! It is not about your little ego-ic you, … It's about You, your greater Self. Give yourself 100% attention and devotion. You surely deserve it!

2. Sit comfortably on the floor or in a chair with your spine straight. As you continue to take meditation vacations, your back muscles will become stronger. We are

so accustomed to slouching that it can be difficult at first. Use a back support if needed.

3. Relax all tension around your physical eyes and forehead. Place soft, easy attention on the area in the middle of your forehead. This is where your pineal gland is located. The pineal gland is shaped like a shriveled little pineapple or pinecone. (Maybe that's why I was inspired in the pineapple fields!) It is referred to as the third eye. It is about the size of a pea, and in the center of the brain it sits in a tiny cave. It is directly behind the eyes and is attached to the third ventricle. While the physiological function of the pineal gland has been unknown until recent times, mystical traditions have long known this area to be the connecting link between the physical and spiritual worlds.

4. With your eyes, forehead and body relaxed, begin just observing your breath —

in and out. Whenever you observe your thoughts taking you somewhere else, lovingly come back to your breath. Even if you start with just five minutes, that is a good beginning. Thank your-Self! You will find yourself wanting to take more vacations and longer vacations every day.

5. Patience is key. Instead of being annoyed at your busy thoughts, detach any judgments and emotions you might have. Try putting on an inner smile. It is like a jump-start into inner peace. Don't take your thoughts too seriously. Very nonchalantly, tell your thoughts as they come up, "oh, ah ha, very interesting but not now." Don't give them any charge and they will finally give up trying to get your attention. Know that where you are going is deeper than your thoughts.

6. Vacation destinations: Have a few special outdoor/nature areas and a special designated area inside. Make it *your* place. Make a little altar by simply covering a

box with a beautiful piece of fabric or a hand-sewn embroidered dishtowel that maybe your great grandma made. Place there a candle, a vase with freshly picked little flowers, a picture of someone who inspires you, a favorite inspirational book, earplugs, incense or oils, a good pillow to sit on, and an instrument or chimes if you have them. Even if you can only play one note, make a beautiful sound unto your-Self! It's a great way to set the tone for your meditation.

Remember, all forms of meditation vacations are good: short ones, long ones, lying-down ones, still ones, motion ones. I like to start my day with a longer one in the early morning and then fill the rest of my day with mini-vacations and meditations in motion. Whenever possible, take them in nature. When you are busy and on the go, just drop in with a deep breath and take a mini-vacation – on the road, at a stoplight, before you start your car, when you first sit up in bed, before you eat, before you meet a friend or have a meeting anytime, anyplace.

A TISKET A TASKET!

SPIRITUAL BENEFITS: Thankfulness, Appreciation

MIND MANTRA:

I gather the blessings of the day

Into my heart basket they will stay

A tisket, a tasket

I will fill up my *whole* basket

And have much to give away!

PHYSICAL BENEFITS: Trunk rotation, strengthening and stretching

DIRECTIONS: Stand with your feet firmly planted about three feet apart and knees slightly bent. The basket is your heart. The blessings are all around you. Gather them up and put them in your heart. Rotating/twisting your body from left to right, with arms swinging horizontally from side to side, scoop the blessings up and put them into your heart. Swing your left hand over across your right side and then bring the blessings back and place them into your heart. Repeat on the other side. Let it become a fluid movement from side to side. Reach out for that blue sky, those white fluffy clouds, the pretty flowers, the fresh air and the people around you who love you. Put them all in your basket. Continue to gather up more and more blessings while you sing or say the mantra. Gather until you know your heart is overflowing. Now you have plenty to give away!

BACK STROKE

SPIRITUAL BENEFITS: Perspective, Self-Acceptance, God-Consciousness

MIND MANTRA:

On my back, I swim, you see

I am a wave in the great big sea

Thee in me

Me in Thee

Hong-Sau!

PHYSICAL BENEFITS: Range of motion and stretching of the shoulder joint. Also helps to improve slumped forward shoulder posture

DIRECTIONS: Standing, alternately circle your arms backward, as if swimming on your back. Repeat mantra.

"We must accept that this creative pulse within us is God's creative pulse itself."
— Joseph Chilton Pearce

BACKWARD OR FORWARD?

(A walking meditation)

SPIRITUAL BENEFIT: Awareness of your thoughts

PHYSICAL BENEFITS: All the health benefits of walking

DIRECTIONS: This is something you can do when you are walking and catch yourself thinking about the past or the future, or doing annoying "reruns" of your worries or unproductive thoughts. When this happens, turn around and walk in the opposite direction, reminding yourself that this is a time to stay focused on the present moment: your breathing, the beauty around you, what you are thankful for.

When you switch back to your agreement of staying in the present, turn back around and proceed forward again.

ANOTHER VARIATION: Instead of turning around and walking the other way, you can just turn around and walk backward. Know that you're leaving these thoughts and worries in the past on the path behind you, and watch them fade in the distance as you walk away from them. Cultivate trust and faith as you take each backward step. Feel the trust and faith for stepping into the uncertainty of life.

"The secret of health for both mind and body is not to mourn for the past, nor to worry about the future, but to live the present moment wisely and earnestly."

— The Buddha

BAMBOO

SPIRITUAL BENEFITS: Flexibility, Even-mindedness, Calmness

MIND MANTRA:

Like bamboo I bend and sway

As changes blow through my way

Like bamboo I bend and sway

As challenges blow through my way

Like bamboo I bend and sway

But my roots in love will stay

PHYSICAL BENEFITS: Core Strengthening, Stretching, Shoulder Stretching

DIRECTIONS: Standing with upright posture, your arms stretching overhead and your tummy tucked in and energized, begin slowly bending from side to side, like bamboo in the wind. Keep your arms reaching upward as they bend from side to side. Feel the roots of your legs and feet firmly planted in the earth. Smile and know that as the challenges and changes of life blow your way, you can be flexible, allowing them to blow through as you keep yourself grounded, stable and calm. Alternate mantra with deep slow breathing.

BE A TREE

SPIRITUAL BENEFIT: Strength, Grounding, Love

MIND MANTRA:

I am strong and grounded like a tree
With unconditional love for me

I am strong and grounded like a tree
With unconditional love for all I see

PHYSICAL BENEFITS: Stretches shoulders and trunk, and strengthens arms and abdominal muscles. Increases lung capacity. Vitalizes the root chakra

DIRECTIONS: If possible stand barefoot by a tree. Like a tree, if you are not strongly rooted, it is difficult to grow. So, plant your feet firmly on the ground, hip-width apart. Stand tall with strong, upright posture and arms at your sides. Energize and stretch your fingers, hands, arms and back as you slowly lift your arms overhead, reaching for the sky. Breathe deeply. Repeat the first line of the mantra. Feel your entire body working, reaching, stretching and strengthening. Feel your ribcage expand. Then slowly, with your arms still energized and strong, bring them down to the horizontal position and repeat the second line of the mantra. Repeat the next verse in the same manner. Continue several times. Then hug a tree and say, "Thank you, sweet tree, for teaching me!"

BLEACH THE TEETH

SPIRITUAL BENEFITS: Spiritual Connection, Happiness, Gratitude

MIND MANTRA:

1)   I smile with all my might

To make my teeth nice and white

And of course, my outlook bright!

2)   Even if I'm feelin' uptight

I put my trust up to the Light

Before I know it, I feel all right!

3)   Even when I'm feelin' down

I put on a smile

And it turns me around

PHYSICAL BENEFITS: Tightens the anti-gravity cheek muscles, diminishes frown lines. Good for the kidneys and liver. And of course…whiter, brighter teeth!

DIRECTIONS: Repeat the verses of the mantra as you put on your biggest smile, exposing your teeth to the sunlight. Although the bleaching process works most rapidly and is most effective when the teeth are exposed directly to the sun, indirect sunlight also works, but you will want to smile a little longer, which isn't such a bad thing! The prescription is for at least five minutes of continual bleaching, working up to 30 minutes. This can be done when you are walking or even driving. (Warning: It is a very contagious exercise so don't be surprised if people approach you and ask what you are so happy about. Just tell them you are bleaching your teeth the natural way. Please be willing to pass along this great information if they seem interested).

23

Although I haven't done extensive research on this, the sun *is* very good at bleaching things, so it makes perfect sense to me! But more importantly, and more instantaneously, is the happiness a smile can bring! Just think of the impact on the world if people would start smiling even five minutes more a day. If the Bible says, "Laughter is the best medicine," then I'd say, "Smiling must be God's second best medicine!"

BRAIN RADIO

(Receiving and transmitting love waves)

SPIRITUAL BENEFITS: Opening your heart and mind to the power of receiving and giving love through your intentions

MIND MANTRA:

I receive love and my heart sings a song

I transmit love and the world sings along

PHYSICAL BENEFITS: Physical healing

DIRECTIONS:

Step 1: With one hand on your heart and the other hand reaching overhead like an antenna receiver, collect all the love, healing and light into your outstretched hand, traveling down your arm and into your heart. Fill up with gratitude. Repeat the first line of the mantra.

Step 2: Switch hands. This time, focus your energy going from your heart and out your antenna arm. Either repeat the second line of the mantra or send out your love, healing and blessings for whomever and whatever comes to your mind.

Example: I send love, light and healing to _____ (fill in with specific names of family, friends, cities, countries, ocean, forests, ozone layer, etc.) As you give, feel the power of love going directly to whom or what you are praying for. Repeat receiving and sending as many times as you like.

BUBBLES

SPIRITUAL BENEFITS: Giving blessings to everyone and everything around you

MIND MANTRA:

Make Bubbles

Not Troubles!

PHYSICAL BENEFITS: Massages the vocal cords. Great for vocal warm-up before speaking or singing

DIRECTIONS: While you are walking along (although it can be done while sitting, driving, working, etc.) begin making a motorboat humming noise with your lips.

Feel as though you are blowing bubbles from your heart and out of your mouth. Fill your bubbles with love and send them to your friends, family, community and the world. Then blow bubbles of healing to those who are sick, to the ocean, to the forests, etc.

With your intention, you can fill your bubbles with whatever you desire and direct them wherever you wish. It is a very quick, concentrated way of sending out your prayers and blessings.

CLAP, CLAP, YAY! YAY!

SPIRITUAL BENEFITS: Strengthens and confirms affirmations and manifestations

PHYSICAL BENEFITS: Increases endorphins

DIRECTIONS: With enthusiasm, clap to life, to love, to you, to me. Clap to whatever you feel excited about and at the same time shout, "YAY! YAY!" Do it with as much enthusiasm as you would after listening to a great live concert. Vocalize what it is you are clapping about. Examples: "Yay to my book being completed!", "Yay to wonderful friends!", "Yay to Spirit guiding me," "Yay to Diesel!" (my faithful dog companion), "Yay to today!" etc., etc.

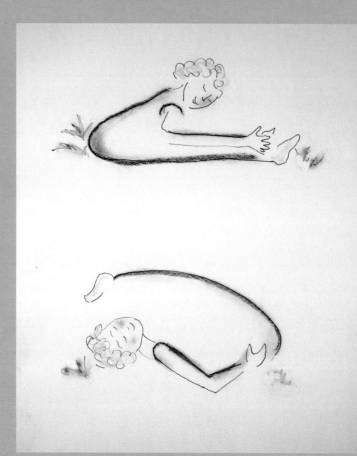

COMPLETION

SPIRITUAL BENEFITS: Persistence, Stamina, Completion, Happiness

MIND MANTRA:

Roll and stretch

Push and press

I will finish

And do my best!

PHYSICAL BENEFITS: Stretches and massages your entire spine and back musculature. Stretches thigh muscles and tones up abdominal muscles. Increases circulation into the head

DIRECTIONS: Lying on your back, roll your feet and legs back over your head. Try to touch your toes on the ground behind your head. Repeat line one of the mantra. Then using the momentum of your legs to roll back over, bring your upper trunk and head up as you stretch your arms and reach for your toes. Repeat line two of the mantra. Repeat line three of the mantra as you are in transition to the feet-over-head position. Go back and forth ten times in a fluid manner.

CRADLE ME

SPIRITUAL BENEFITS: Forgiveness, Self-Affirmation, Comfort, Any other inner-child nurturing that needs to be done

MIND MANTRA:

Like a nest up in the tree

Life supports and cradles me

PHYSICAL BENEFITS: Abdominal oblique strengthening and stretching

(Sometimes I look back and remember how sweet and comforting it was when I would lay my head on my mother's lap and she would sweetly caress my face and comb her fingers through my hair. I cherish those memories. Raising four kids kept me busy rocking, hugging, and nurturing. They are all grown and gone now and I realize I could use some nurturing myself! We all have that inner child who could use sweet cradling and affirmation that we are appreciated and that all is well. So, if there isn't anyone around to rock and cradle you, do it to yourself!)

DIRECTIONS: Position your arms as if you were cradling a baby — yourself! With knees softly bent, use your abdominal oblique (twisting) muscles to make controlled twisting movements with your trunk and arms. Transfer weight from side to side, and freely move arms in a figure-eight pattern. Continue until you feel full with some good loving!

CRAWLING AROUND UPSIDE DOWN

SPIRITUAL BENEFIT: Mental strength and stamina. Going beyond mental weakness and limited beliefs

MIND MANTRA:

Crawling around, upside down

Doing what I never knew I could do!

All because of the power of *You!*

PHYSICAL BENEFITS: Strengthens your core abdominal muscles

DIRECTIONS: Lying on your back, keep your lower spine glued to the ground. (Eliminate the arch in low back). With arms and legs in an upside-down crawling position, pretend you are crawling on a ceiling. Always keep your focus on your lower back, using your abdominal muscles to press your lower back flat on the floor. Repeat until your abdominals start to give up and your back wants to arch. To increase the physical challenge you can always move your arms and legs in various patterns together or opposing; symmetrical, diagonal or circular motions. Work up to about 20 repetitions of each variation. It feels good to follow with the Cobra exercise, and then just lie on your back in the soft grass and relax as you watch the clouds go by.

FIGURE 8'S

(Walking meditation)

SPIRITUAL BENEFIT: Balance and connection of our human, earthly roots and our heavenly origin

MIND MANTRA:

As I connect to earth below, I am grounded

As I connect to heaven above, I am guided

As we meet in the middle, I am strong, fit, and able

DIRECTIONS: I like to do this one when I am walking in the sand at the beach. I will take a stick and draw a big figure eight in the sand.

I will then slowly start walking the figure eight, repeating the mantra. When I get in the middle, I hold my hands together in a strong fisted position in front of my abdomen and recite the last line. You can also draw in the dirt or just use an imaginary line.

"I honor you as kings and queens, gods and goddesses of royalty, and wish you divine balance and mastery of your earthly roots and heavenly spirit."
— Heidi Hohani

FLOWER POWER

(Walking meditation)

SPIRTUAL BENEFIT: Connects to inner-guidance and the Divine in nature

MIND MANTRA:

Little Flower

I love you so

Tell me what

I need to know

DIRECTIONS: While slowly walking, be fully present and breathe in nature all around you.

Notice the simple beauty in the little weed flowers growing in the cracks or alongside the road that you usually would just walk by. Pick them and begin making a little bouquet with these beautiful little flowers. You might even tie them together with a skinny, flexible leaf. Continue to walk as you appreciate your bouquet of flowers. Gaze at your flowers and know they are each a gift from God. Ask each little flower for a special message as you repeat the mantra. Be still and listen. Their special message just for you will come to your mind. After each flower has given you a message, take a moment to be thankful. When you get home put your flowers in a little vase to remind you throughout the day that God is always with you, in you, around you, and *is* you. You can also lie down and put your bouquet on your heart and breathe in all the beauty and special messages that were given to you, or give them to a friend or stranger.

FLYING HIGH

SPIRITUAL BENEFITS: Perspective, Freedom, Self-expression

MIND MANTRA:
Flying High
I am a bird up in the sky
I am free
I am free
To be exactly who I am meant to be
Me!

When I'm tired
I see as I soar
That in this life
There is so much more!

PHYSICAL BENEFITS: Strengthens arm muscles

DIRECTIONS: With shoulders, elbows, wrists and fingers loose and flowing, make graceful "wing" movements with your arms and repeat the first part of the mantra. When your arms begin getting too tired, go into "soar" mode, keeping your arms horizontally straight. Repeat the second half of the mantra. Pretend you are looking down on your life and getting a different perspective from a greater height. Return to the up-and-down movements of your arms again when you're ready. Go from pumping wings to soar mode, back and forth a couple times. As your wings get stronger and your thoughts grander, you will be flying in new, unknown, exciting territory!

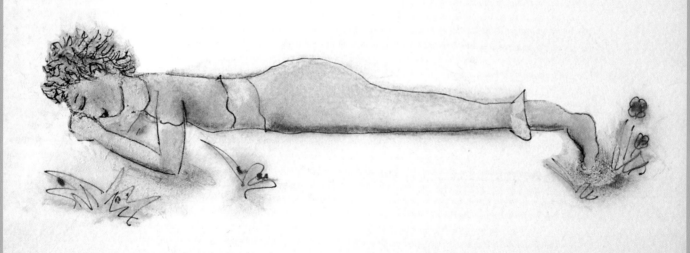

GOOD TO THE CORE!

SPIRITUAL BENEFITS: Faith

MIND MANTRA:

I pray for faith

"Give me more!" I implore!

On this I concentrate

As I strengthen my core

PHYSICAL BENEFITS: Shoulder and core strengthening

DIRECTIONS: Lie low in a "tabletop" or plank position.

Have your hands in a folded prayer position right below your forehead. Your forearms and folded hands will be directly below your head and shoulders in an inverted "V" position. Your weight will be distributed between the balls of your feet and your forearms. Keep your back flat. Hold your stomach and core area tightly as you repeat the mantra. Increase the duration of this exercise as you are able. Always train, don't strain.

"Let us have faith that right makes might, and in that faith let us to the end dare to do our duty as we understand it. I am conscious every moment that all I am and all I have are subject to the control of a Higher Power, and that Power can use me or not use me in any manner and at any time as in His wisdom might be pleasing to Him."
— Abraham Lincoln

HACK THE TRASH

SPIRITUAL BENEFITS: Consciously letting go of limiting beliefs, ideas, negative feelings and thoughts

MIND MANTRA:

I hack up all of my mental trash

And it quickly transforms with a golden flash

PHYSICAL BENEFITS: Range of motion of the shoulder joint

DIRECTIONS: I call "trash" any limiting thoughts, beliefs or judgments that you are running over and over in your mind — either about yourself or someone else — or any negative thinking that is taking priority and keeping you from being content, confident, trusting and peaceful. I like to do this one as I walk along. Sometimes it is fun to use a little stick that you find lying on the path as your sword. Starting with your right arm, raise it up over your head and bring it down, as if you were trying to slice a diagonal cut in a watermelon. Let it return in the opposite diagonal pattern. Do this several times and then repeat on other side. You can also do this while holding your sword with both hands. When you have any limiting thoughts, judgments or other "should, could or would have" statements floating around in your mind, free yourself of them by taking the sword of golden light to them!

HERE I AM!

(A walking meditation)

SPIRITUAL BENEFIT: Recognition and awareness that God expresses Him/Herself everywhere and in everything.

MIND MANTRA:

"Here I AM, Here I AM, Here…I…*AM*"
(Repeat several times and then add the following lines when you experience them)
"I can see you!" or "I can feel you!" or "I can hear you!" or "I can breathe you!"

DIRECTIONS: If your connection to Spirit is feeling a little weak, this is a good one to wake it up.

As you are slowly walking, begin singing (or saying) the first line of the mantra. As your gaze stops at a little flower, the blue sky, the ocean, etc., interject, "I can feel you!" or "I can hear you!", etc.

"Their minstrels play music from within; and whole oceans of passion foam on the crest of the waves."

— Rumi Jallaludin

HI-CHI

SPIRITUAL BENEFITS: Freedom of expression

MIND MANTRA:

I will move free as the breeze

As the Spirit of love dances through me

PHYSICAL BENEFITS: Flexibility, Balance, Range of Motion, Strength

DIRECTIONS: Below is just my story for this free-moving exercise. I named it after myself. If there is any truth to it, I really don't know!

Hi-Chi is where movement and dance originated. It was from a time when there was no fear or greed. Slow, focused, flowing movement was a form of meditation everyone freely engaged in. It was a way of uniting body and Spirit, and a natural way to express gratitude. There was no right or wrong way to move, no teachers or guides. Each person expressed their movements freely from their heart. Then came separation and fear. Along with it came aggression. The movements became methodical techniques for self-defense and warfare. They were sometimes disguised in the slow beautiful movements, but now each move had its secret underlying aggressive motive. The beauty and freedom of Hi-Chi was forgotten. Now is the time of its return! Be free! Stand barefoot on the land. Move to the sound of the symphony in and all around you. Be one with the wind, the sunshine and the rain. Be the beauty that is all around you. Feel and express your joy with your spontaneous movement. Let your heart sing, "I am joy-filled and grateful!" No rules, no right or wrong — just you! Move free!

HONG-SAU QUICK STEP

SPIRITUAL BENEFITS: Cleansing, Purification, Connection to Spirit

MIND MANTRA:

Hong-Sau

(English translation: Thee in me, Me in Thee. Pronounced "hung-saw")

PHYSICAL BENEFITS: Improves cardiac/aerobic fitness, lowers blood pressure and anxiety levels

DIRECTIONS: Although most of my walking meditations are done at a very slow pace, this one is done very briskly to add more aerobics to my exercise.

I begin by putting on my imaginary crown. I align my body with my best posture (as described in the Royal Promenade exercise). I begin walking, breathing deeply and feeling gratitude in my heart. Keeping my elbows bent at around 90 degrees, I swing them back and forth as I walk briskly. My breathing pattern keeps in time with my steps. I inhale through my nose for four strides while thinking, "HONG" and then exhale through my mouth for the next four strides as I think "SAU." As my breathing and heart begin to get a little more challenged and begin to work harder, I just keep focusing on the rhythm of my steps and "HONG-SAU." With the blood circulating life throughout my body, I imagine the healing power of the Divine permeating every cell.

I KICK MYSELF!

SPIRITUAL BENEFITS: Encouragement

MIND MANTRA:
I kick myself in the booty
To remind me I am a cutie-patootie!

PHYSICAL BENEFITS: Stimulates the bladder and gallbladder meridian, increases range of motion to ankle joints, and circulates energy flow down into legs and feet

DIRECTIONS: While lying on your back, bring your knees up to a chest position. Begin alternately kicking your heels into your bottom as vigorously as you can. Continue for several minutes. Repeat the mantra as you kick.

I SURRENDER

SPIRITUAL BENEFITS: Surrender, Humility

MIND MANTRA:

I surrender into the arms of Love

PHYSICAL BENEFITS: Stretches shoulders, upper back and hamstrings. Increases circulation into the face and head

DIRECTIONS: With your legs wide apart, grasp your hands behind your back, keeping your arms straight. Bend your body forward, dropping your head down in between your legs. Lift hands and arms up over your head as far as possible. If you are unable to do this with your hands clasped, you can use a strap or a towel.

As you are hanging upside down, softly and slowly repeat the mantra over and over again. You can also slowly lower your grasped hands and lift them back and forth and side to side for a little additional shoulder stretch.

"If you forget yourself, you become the universe."
— Hakuin Ortegama

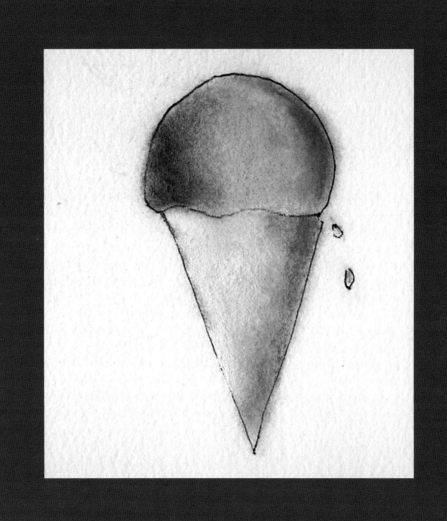

ICE CREAM CONE MORNING

SPIRITUAL BENEFITS: Joy, Thankfulness, Appreciation, Sensuality, Passion

MIND MANTRA:

Today is a beautiful, delicious *ice cream cone* morning!

I stretch out my tongue to savor the licks and catch all the drips!

PHYSICAL BENEFITS: Stretches the esophageal nerve and tongue muscles

DIRECTIONS: In the morning, go out in nature and savor the beauty all around you. Notice the incredible deliciousness of it all, like the most amazing ice cream *cone* you've ever had!

Go ahead and stick your tongue out as far as you can and take the biggest, juiciest licks of this most delicious *ice cream cone morning.*

Slurp it up! Lick it up! Let the passion overtake you — the beautiful blue sky, the fresh air, the green trees and the flowers. Making your own sound effects is always a plus! I know this may feel a bit strange, a bit sensual and maybe even passionate and exciting but isn't *life* exactly that?

IT'S THE TWINKLE

SPIRITUAL BENEFITS: Self-Love, Acceptance

MIND MANTRA:
What counts is not the wrinkle
But my loving kindness and the twinkle!
Or
I would really like to boast
It's not the wrinkle in the thigh
But the twinkle in the eye
That really matters most!

PHYSICAL BENEFITS: Improves vision

DIRECTIONS: Using a mirror, gaze into your eyes. See the twinkle and the beauty of who you really are. Give yourself plenty of time and don't stop looking until you truly see the beauty and love gazing back at you. Lovingly accept any signs of aging you might see and look past that. Forgive yourself for any resentment, anger or sadness you might see. You are new, like the day. Keep looking deeper until you see the beauty shining forth. If you need additional support getting there, try cracking a little smile on your face. (Smiles connect you to your soul and allow the beauty of your soul to shine forth.)

JOG FOR THE JIGGLE OF IT

SPIRITUAL BENEFITS: The clearing of mind clutter

MIND MANTRA:

I jog for the jiggle of it!

HO HO HO! I let it all go!

I jog for the joy of it!

HO HO HO! I let it all go!

I jog for the fun of it!

HO HO HO! I let it all go!

PHYSICAL BENEFITS: Increases circulation, Relaxes tension, Strengthens urinary muscles, Helps with elimination

One of the best ways to promote healing of any condition is to improve circulation to the involved region, both to carry nutrients to the area as well as to carry away wastes and by-products.

DIRECTIONS: When I am feeling I have too much clutter on my mind or tension in my body, I like to use this exercise. It shakes all the old, recycled thoughts, worries and tensions that have settled or stuck onto my body and mind. My body and mind then have room for fresh oxygenated blood, healing power and creative thoughts to infuse me. When stressful thoughts and worries sit around in us for too long, they not only clutter our mind but they also accumulate in our shoulders, stomachs and various other body parts and cause constriction from the vital flow of energy.
If left unattended, they collect and manifest as pain and dysfunction.
If you are not a jogger, don't worry, I'm not either. It's not the jog but the jiggle

you're after with this exercise. You just want to step it up a bit so it gives you more of a jiggle than what a walk can give. Mentally scan your body and see what tension you can consciously let go. Then scan your thoughts and do the same thing. Work your jiggle till you feel you have had a good washing or clearing. Focus on the jiggle of it. If your mind wanders, bring it back to the jiggle. It helps to keep the mantra going with a rhythmical beat.

JUST SITTIN'!

SPIRTUAL BENEFITS: Connection to Divine Consciousness, Calmness, Focus, Peace

MIND MANTRA:

Hong (Thee in Me)

Sau (Me in Thee)

PHYSICAL BENEFITS: Strengthens back muscles, reduces physical stress and rest-lessness, lowers blood pressure and anxiety

DIRECTIONS: This exercise reminds me of when I was a little girl and my mom would have me stand in a corner if I were misbehaving usually due to fighting with my brother! So we would stand in a corner until our emotions would calm down and we could make up and be friends. I might not be fighting with my brother anymore but I continue to have uptight, unproductive misbehavior thoughts that cause me to worry, fret and become anxious. Stress! Too many projects, to-do lists, deadlines and responsibilities. When I find myself getting a little snappy, it is a sure sign that I need to put myself "in the corner" and just start sittin! Usually, it is when we feel we don't have enough time to just sit that we really need it most of all.

So, get yourself to a nice place to just sit and begin focusing on your breathing. There are many breathing patterns and exercises one can do, but an easy favorite of mine is to inhale for five seconds, hold breath for five seconds, exhale for five seconds and then keep the breath out for five seconds. Continue this pattern for approximately ten repetitions. Adjust your count so it is comfortable but just a little stretch. After you have done ten repetitions, return to normal breathing. Your breathing should feel deeper and more relaxed. As you are enjoying this relaxed state, meditate on the meaning of Hong-Sau: "God is within you and you are within God. Thee in Me, Me in Thee." That is more important than anything else. Set your priority of God first no matter what. Feel the calmness spread within you. Thank yourself for remembering to come back to your center and tell yourself that you will now proceed with your day in a calm, trusting and yet active manner. Surrender to the fact that all things will be taken care of in the right order and in the right timing. Hong-Sau!

KNEE TO CHEST

SPIRITUAL BENEFIT: Faith in Co-creation

MIND MANTRA:
Knee to Chest
I will do my best
And God will do the rest

PHYSICAL BENEFITS: Stimulates balance, stretches hip muscles, strengthens legs and ankles

DIRECTIONS: Standing with upright posture, lift your knee up to your chest, holding your leg just below the knee. Maintain strong, upright balanced posture as you repeat the mantra.

Alternate the mantra with silent deep breaths. Repeat several times on each leg. Modify if it is too difficult. If you are unable to bring your knee to your chest, then bring your hip and knee to a 90-degree angle. Feel free to personalize each exercise, always being gentle and positive with yourself. You may also do this lying down for just a hip stretch.

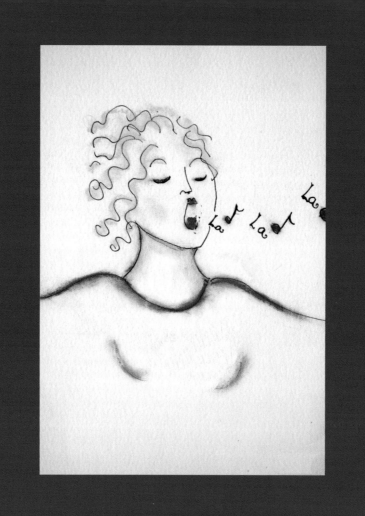

LA-LA-LA!

(A walking or sitting meditation)

SPIRITUAL BENEFIT: Allows your inner Self to freely express its happiness and joy. Sometimes we have difficulty expressing how we truly feel. This exercise helps to free blocked emotions and makes it easier to express your true inner-being.

MIND MANTRA:

La la la! La la la la la la la!

PHYSICAL BENEFITS: Exercises the vocal cords and releases blocked energy in the throat

DIRECTIONS: Begin with just some simple LA-LA-LAs. Compose a little tune with a few notes. Don't pass any judgment on your song or your voice. Just keep it simple and keep singing LA-LAs. You are an integral part of the symphony of life! This can also be done when driving your car. I surprise myself with how much fun I can have when I turn off my CD player or radio and just begin singing whatever spontaneously comes up. You don't have to be a good singer. Just appreciate that you have a voice! I also like to do this one in conjunction with the "Bleach Your Teeth" exercise. They go so well together.

LIKE A SNAIL
(A walking meditation)

SPIRITUAL BENEFITS: Appreciation of the present moment

MIND MANTRA:

Like a snail I will go very, very, very slow

There is magic in the moment

In this moment there is magic

PHYSICAL BENEFITS: Relaxation, Deep Breathing

DIRECTIONS: Wherever you are (of course it is best out in a beautiful place in nature), begin walking as slow you can and take special notice of what you see.

Then notice what your ears can hear. How far can you hear? Then notice what you physically feel. Feel not only the sensations on the outside of your body, such as the breeze brushing your skin, but also tune in to the sensation of your feet being placed on the ground, the articulation of your ankle bones, your chest rising and falling with your breath. Is there any excess tension in your shoulders, face or neck that you can let go? Breathe slowly and deeply. Make many stops to observe nature around you. Feel the blessings in the moment. Repeat the mantra slowly and calmly.

forgivness
grace
Peace
health
Spirit
freedom
beauty
gratitude
Love
friendship
Compassion

THE MAGIC STRAW

(A lying or walking meditation)

SPIRITUAL BENEFITS: Love, Happiness, Joy, Peace, Abundance, Comfort, Forgiveness, Humility, Healing, Relaxation

MIND MANTRA:

I breathe in_____ (fill in the spiritual benefit you desire) and it permeates every part of me

PHYSICAL BENEFITS: Lowers anxiety and blood pressure level. Induces overall relaxation

DIRECTIONS: Lying comfortably on your back, close your eyes and begin to imagine: Your lips are pursed around a magic straw. This magic straw goes up beyond the clouds (that represent worry, fear, doubt, lack, etc.). This magic straw goes all the way up where there is only bright blue sky. In the bright blue sky are bundles of gifts for you. Free! There are gifts of love, abundance, health, happiness, joy, creativity and more. Each is wrapped in pretty bright colors. Inhale with softly pursed lips the gift of your choice. The deeper you breathe, the more you are allowing into your being. Take a long, slow and deep breath, feeling the color of the gift as it fills the core of your being. Pause at the top of your inhalation. Relax as you slowly begin to exhale, feeling the color and quality showering and soaking into every cell of your body. Continue with as many gifts as you desire. Notice if a little smile begins to form on your face. When you feel satisfied and full, rest peacefully, returning to your normal breathing. Feel gratitude in your heart.

MANA IN Mi MANO

(God's power in my hands)

SPIRITUAL BENEFITS: Strength, Power, Right action

MIND MANTRA:

With all that my hands do today,

May they be a blessing in every way

PHYSICAL BENEFITS: Stretches the overworked muscles of the forearm, wrist and fingers in the opposite direction of how they usually work. Increases the circulation, flushing out old blood, bringing in the new. Relaxes the tension in the forearm, hand and finger muscles

DIRECTIONS: Standing or sitting straight and tall, stretch out your left arm in front of your body with the palm facing up. With your right hand, stretch the left fingers and wrist downward or in an extended position. Hold the stretch and breathe deeply as you invite and feel the power of life enter the palm of your hand, fingers, wrist and arm. Slowly bring the outstretched palm to your mouth as you repeat the mantra and complete it by exhaling your breath into your hand as a blessing. Repeat three times and then do it on your other side.

MEET IN THE MIDDLE

SPIRITUAL BENEFIT: Balance

MIND MANTRA:

My roots grow deep

My branches reach high

They meet in the middle

And make me fit as a fiddle

PHYSICAL BENEFITS: Stretches upper extremities and trunk muscles

DIRECTIONS: Stand upright with feet hip-width apart, one arm reaching energetically upward while the other arm is reaching energetically downward.

Repeat the first half of the mantra. Then, bring both hands together in a fisted position in front of your lower abdominal area. Repeat the second half of the mantra. Repeat as many times as desired. This one is a nice follow-up after "The Tree" exercise.

"The best and safest thing is to keep a balance in your life, acknowledge the great powers around us and in us. If you can do that, and live that way, you are really a wise man."

— Euripides

MONGOOSE to MARIGOLD

I frequently walk through the pineapple fields with my rather *large* and very *strong* dog, Diesel. I keep him on a leash by my side and for the most part he is very sweet and obedient. However, sometimes I can be calmly walking along and before I can blink an eye all havoc breaks loose! He spies a mongoose and he turns into a ravaging beast! He practically drags me through the fields in pursuit of the mongoose. After much work and aggravation, I get him back under control. Scolding him, I dust myself off and emphatically shout, *"No! Don't chase the mongoose!"*

I see it as a lesson for me. I often do the same thing with my thoughts. Faster than I can blink my eye, I can let a crazy, unproductive thought into my consciousness and it begins to take over. If I don't choose to replace it with a better thought ASAP, it will most likely drag me into unwanted territory.

So, I have developed a sharp eye for those sneaky mongooses and emphatically tell myself, "*No!* I'm not going to chase that mongoose!" By taking some deep breaths of love into the crazy thoughts, I transform them into more constructive, positive thoughts. Turn your mongooses into beautiful marigolds!

NUMBER 4

SPIRITUAL BENEFIT: Clarification of who you are and what your purpose is

MIND MANTRA: I am for _____. (Fill in whatever comes freely to your mind. Keep repeating with something different every time. Example: I am for Love, I am for Peace, I am for Fun, I am for Laughter, I am for Beauty, I am for Shining, I am for taking care of myself, I am for clear, honest communication.)

PHYSICAL BENEFITS: Stretches and increases circulation into your hip muscles, which is good also for your low back

DIRECTIONS: Lie on your back, with knees bent and feet on the ground.

Place your right ankle against your left thigh, above your left knee. The right knee will point to the right. Lifting up your left knee, place your right hand and arm through the triangular space that your legs are making and grasp your hands together around back of your left thigh. Your right elbow can gently push against your right thigh to give it more stretch. Your lower left leg can alternate between a straight leg position (which would be straight up and down) or be left in the bent-knee position, parallel to the ground. You should see a "number 4" configuration that your legs are making in this position. Feel the stretch in your right buttock and hip as you relax and say all the things that you are "for." Rest and repeat on the other side.

ON SACRED GROUND

SPIRITUAL BENEFITS: Spiritual connection, Grounding, Perspective, Deceleration

MIND MANTRA:

On sacred earth I lay

Blessed be this holy day

PHYSICAL BENEFITS: Relaxation, Lowers blood pressure, Decreases anxiety

DIRECTIONS: Find yourself a nice comfortable place in nature to take off your shoes and lie down for a few minutes. Look at the sky, watch the clouds go by, feel the beautiful earth beneath.

If I have had a busy day, I love to end my afternoon with this exercise to help me once again slow down and just appreciate the gift of life. Begin breathing and enjoying. Even if you are not in the most ideal natural setting, you can usually find some special little spot. One day while waiting for my oil to be changed at Walmart, instead of sticking around inside the noisy, air-conditioned store, I found the parking lot out back where all the big container trucks were parked. There wasn't any traffic and there were no people going by. There was a little grassy area nestled in between the big containers. It gave me just enough privacy, blue sky, green grass and a slight breeze so I could lie down, relax and feel my connection with Earth.

ON YOUR MARK, GET SET, GO!

SPIRITUAL BENEFITS: Setting your priority, Putting the Divine first in your life, Enthusiasm, Passion

MIND MANTRA:

Hey Ho! I'm smart you know

I line up my heart

Putting you (God) at the start

Hey, Ho! This is the way

I choose to go!

PHYSICAL BENEFITS: Strengthens your lower leg muscles, Improves balance, offers a nice stretch and range of motion of the shoulder joints

DIRECTIONS: Standing with your feet hip-width apart, focus your energy down your straight legs and arms. Lift up and down on the balls of your feet, while at the same time waving your arms up and down like starting flags at a race. Repeat the mantra.

OPEN HEART

SPIRITUAL BENEFIT: Peace, Hope, Tranquility

MIND MANTRA:

I open my heart

And lean back into love

I let peace reign in my life

Like a dove

PHYSICAL BENEFITS: Improves slumped shoulder, neck and upper back posture. Strengthens the upper back that gets weak and stretched out from poor posture

DIRECTIONS: Fold your hands behind the back of your head. Tuck your chin in. With the back of your spine elongated, begin with your elbows together and your chin toward your chest. As you begin to inhale, slowly open and spread your elbows apart, squeezing your shoulder blades together. Speak the first line of the mantra. Then begin arching backward with your elbows wide apart. Feel your chest and heart open. Speak the second line of the mantra. Continue to stay in this open stretched position and then speak the third line of the mantra. Slowly return to starting position with your head flexed forward and elbows together. Do it several times.

PALM TREE LOVE

"The righteous shall flourish like the Palm Tree."
Psalms 92:12

SPIRITUAL BENEFITS: Faith, Trust, Balance

MIND MANTRA:

From my center I get my start
And learn to trust with all my heart

Or

Like a Palm Tree
My strength comes from my core
My core is rooted deep in love

PHYSICAL BENEFITS: Leg and core strength, balance

DIRECTIONS: Standing rigid and tall, place your hands in prayer position and place the sole of one foot against the inner thigh of the opposite leg. (If this is too difficult, balance sole of foot on lower leg.) Breathe deeply and focus, keeping your balance as long as you can and repeating the mantra. Change sides and repeat.

"The life of a devotee of Christ Consciousness, comes from the life of Love implanted in the heart."

— Author Unknown

PUMPIN' IN DA LOVE!

SPIRITUAL BENEFITS: Love, Healing

MIND MANTRA:

Like a pump

I arch and squeeze

Pushing love

Down to my back and knees!

PHYSICAL BENEFITS: This is a very good exercise for the health of your back and your vertebral discs. We spend the majority of our day bending our trunk forward - driving, cooking, sitting over the computer, lifting and bending.

This exercise helps to balance this out by bending backward. Also, try to remember to just arch backward throughout the day.

DIRECTIONS: Start in kneeling position with body and head folded down to your knees, arms stretched out in front. Begin to slowly lunge upper body forward while extending back, bringing chest forward and bringing head and gaze upward. Alternate from the flexed to this arched extended position. Leave hands in the same position as you alternate between poses. Repeat at least ten times and alternate the mantra with deep breathing.

RENDEZVOUS WITH YOU

SPIRITUAL BENEFITS: Energy, Peace and Healing

MIND MANTRA:

Your love illuminates me

Your light heals me

Shine on me, shine on me

PHYSICAL BENEFITS: Calms sympathetic nervous system, Lowers blood pressure, Vitamin D absorption for bones and teeth, Energizes, Boosts the immune system, Improves psychological health

DIRECTIONS: This is one of my favorites; after just a few minutes it makes me feel so good. Make a date with the Sun as She makes her morning arrival! Somewhere beautiful and private in nature is ideal. Get your clothes and backpack ready the night before and let the excitement begin to stir in your heart as you fall asleep. Of course, the Sun loves those spur-of-the-moment rendezvous, when you just pull your car over on the side of the road or run out on your grass with your night-clothes still on. She loves to greet you as much as you love to greet Her. The prime time to really have an intimate rendezvous with the Sun — when you can really gaze into Her eyes, so to speak — is during the first 30-60 minutes of her arrival in the morning. After that, she can get a little too strong for the human eye, so I gaze through closed eyelids or direct my gaze away from the Sun. I find that a few minutes of early morning sungazing feels incredibly healing. It boosts me spiritually, mentally and physically. It is a very ancient practice and, for most of us in our culture, a forgotten one. So, wherever She finds you, a romantic nature spot or not, know that your meeting place, wherever it may be, is PERFECT for that moment. If you are driving, pull your car over and stop for a moment. With a thankful heart, drop your mental baggage and open your being to the Sun. Stretch your arms out wide above you. Absorb the beautiful rays like a sponge. Repeat the mantra as you intersperse it with deep breaths. As other people notice you taking time to enjoy and remember, it will help them to take time to enjoy and remember also. We are here to help each other remember who we are: Children of the One God. When you feel full, complete your rendezvous by placing your hands over your heart in gratitude. Other nice complementary exercises to add to it are: Rolling Eyeballs, I Surrender and The Cobra.

REPEAT THAT

(a walking meditation)

SPIRITUAL BENEFIT: Reinforces and manifests positive attributes, thoughts and intentions in your physical reality

MIND MANTRA:

Any of your favorite quotes. Here are two of mine:

"This moment is all there is."

— Rumi

"Let the beauty we love, be what we do."

— Rumi

Or choose a longer one, such as:

"As I consciously move through this day, my purpose is to be mindful of the presence of power within and put it into practice. As I make choices along the way, I am responsible for what I choose to think about and how I react to what is taking place in my experience. I know spirit guides me with great joy. No matter where I am, I am always in the right place at the right time, doing what is right for me to do. I allow Love, Wisdom, Compassion, Goodness full expression in my life."

— Author Unknown

PHYSICAL BENETFITS: Improves memory and all the many benefits of walking

DIRECTIONS: Choose an inspirational quote or a positive affirmation. Write it on a little index card or paper. Tuck it into your pocket while you are on your walk. Begin by slowly repeating the first two or three words as you walk. Slowly add

more words. Speak the words in time with your footsteps.
Every time you repeat the quote, go deeper with it. Feel it, trust it and believe it.
Feel it as a part of you.

Just a little note on Walking Meditations:
Walking Meditations are a one-on-one, special time for you. Always keep on your
toes for surprises, lessons and ideas that your Self might be trying to reveal to you.
Remember it is not how far or fast you walk, but how deeply you stay focused in
the now. Just like taking a good walk with a friend, if you give each other your total
attention, the walk is really enjoyable and you learn a lot about each other. I find
that my Self is quite playful, creative and, of course, very ingenious!

ROLLING EYEBALLS

SPIRITUAL BENEFITS: Healing light

MIND MANTRA:

I roll my eyeballs

Up and down

And all around

Opening them

Big and bright

Letting in the *Sun's*

Healing light.

PHYSICAL BENEFITS: Physical healing to all areas of your body, eye strengthening

DIRECTIONS: Opening your eyes as wide as you can while in the sunlight, begin making slow, big circles. Do about five in each direction and then from side to side, starting at the top of your eye socket and slowly moving your gaze down to the bottom of your eye socket. It should take about five repetitions of going back and forth to go from the top to the bottom. Finish by doing diagonal patterns, left upper corner to right lower corner and then right upper corner to left bottom corner. Your eye, as does the bottom of your foot, has reflexology that corresponds to all the areas of your body.

ROYAL PROMENADE

(a walking meditation)

SPIRITUAL BENEFITS: Lightness of Heart, Positive Attitude, Thankfulness and Vitality

MIND MANTRA:

I *am* a Royal One

You know

Happy and proud

I walk like so

PHYSICAL BENEFITS: Correct posture improves neck, low back and shoulder problems

DIRECTIONS: This exercise is all about posture and feeling beautiful. Beautiful posture innately begins from an inwardly happy heart, which is then reflected as a beautiful glowing, strong stature on the outside. It's so magical that when you are in a less than desirable mood, if you just take a little effort to make a few exterior adjustments, you can jump-start your mood back to a happier, sweeter state! So, it is good to work your posture from both angles, inside and out. It reduces the law of gravity both in a physical and in an emotional way!

Begin your Royal Promenade by using your imagination and placing the most beautiful crown on top of your head. How beautiful and creative can you make your crown? Every day create a new beautiful crown; it only takes a few seconds of imagination. Example of my crown today: a brilliant blue, sea-glass crown covered with diamond sparkles like the sunlight dancing on the ocean. My first crown began in the pineapple fields as a beautiful green one with a bright pink pineapple blossom in the center. So, once you have your crown on, stand proud and straight, shoulders back, chin tucked slightly in with ears aligned over shoulders (eliminating the forward head and slouched shoulder posture), chest light and open, beaming out rays of light! The abdominal area is softly lifted to support your naturally arched low back curve. Now the final touches — a smile on your face and a twinkle in your eye! (If you are not feeling a real smile yet, add the "Bleach the Teeth" exercise. It won't be long until that smile is connected to your soul and your true joy is shining through.) As you walk, feel as though you are on top of the world, full of gratitude, vitality and appreciation for every breath you take. Remember the beautiful crown that you are wearing. Whenever you're feeling a frown, remember to "Put on your beautiful crown!"

RUB IT IN!

SPIRITUAL BENEFITS: Connection of body, mind and Spirit. Promotes love and gratitude unto thy Self and the gift of experiencing being alive in a human body

MIND MANTRA:

Rub-a-dub-dub

I give myself love

PHYSICAL BENEFITS: Increases circulation and relaxation, Physical healing

DIRECTIONS: With the intention of sending love and healing into your body, give yourself little body rubs. Listen to your body. Maybe one day your knees might want a little attention, another day it may be your heart or your toes. Pamper yourself with a little rub-a-dub-dub love.

"There is no remedy for love but to love more."
– Henry David Thoreau

SEARCH ME!

SPIRITUAL BENEFITS: Cleansing and purification

MIND MANTRA:

Search me

Purge me

Immerse me in Your love.

Wash me clean

Like in a washing machine!

PHYSICAL BENEFITS: Energizes and strengthens the entire body, increases circulation throughout body

DIRECTIONS: Stand with your back to the Sun, legs hip-width apart, arms stretched overhead. Tighten and contract your arms all the way to your fingertips and from your stomach and buttocks all the way down your legs. Repeat the first three lines of the mantra. Then drop your arms and begin shaking your whole body as you repeat the last two lines of the mantra.

SHAKE IT UP BABY!

SPIRITUAL BENEFIT: Peace, Energy, Gratitude, Happiness

MIND MANTRA:

Shake, Jiggle and Jive

Hallelujah!

Shake, Jiggle and Jive

I am alive!

PHYSICAL BENEFITS: Decreases tension, Promotes muscular relaxation, Increases circulation, Massages the organs, Increases elimination of toxins, Tones the bladder and kidneys

(Stress is the leading cause (75-90%) of health problems. Stress is the body's reaction to perceptions.)

DIRECTIONS: While singing the mantra, begin wiggling and jiggling every body part that you can. Just start shaking it up! Keep it up for five minutes or more if you can. When you sing or say "Hallelujah," lift hands up overhead while you continue to shake them. End by placing your hands over your heart and being still and feeling the increased circulation and energy running through your whole body. Feel happy and thankful.

SING YOUR NAME

(a walking meditation)

SPIRITUAL BENEFIT: Compassion, Self-love

MIND MANTRA: (Your name sung sweetly over and over again)

PHYSICAL BENEFITS: Exercises your vocal chords

DIRECTIONS: In Hawaii, it is a common custom to give yourself a new name or a nickname, a name that describes you, sounds sweet to you, expresses you, such as: Ocean, Mele, Windcloud, Vision, etc. What name would you love to have? What name would best describe you? What name just feels wonderful to say?

If you absolutely love and resonate with your birth/given name, great! This exercise helps you to let go of any old attachments that you may have associated with your name. Like the morning, you are new every day. Once you have a name that you like, begin sweetly singing it over and over again. After you sing your own name, it's great to also sing the names of your family and friends as you send love to them. Then sing to those you have had your challenges with – it may open your heart and allow deeper understanding.

SPIRALING

SPIRITUAL BENEFITS: Recognition of our inner matrix of love

MIND MANTRA:

I spiral to the center of my being

And there I find

Love, Joy and Peace of Mind

PHYSICAL BENEFITS: Range of motion of cervical, thoracic and lumbar spine

DIRECTIONS: Standing with your legs hip-width apart, begin slowly rotating your head in circles.

If you had an imaginary paintbrush sticking out of the top of your head, begin painting beautiful, smooth circles in the sky. Start with small circles and enlarge them as big as you comfortably can. Begin repeating the mantra. Feel your trunk and your hips begin to organically flow in the opposite circular direction. After several minutes, stop and reverse the direction. When you have completed both directions, stop, place hands over heart and feel the stillness and peace.

SUPERCHARGED!

SPIRITUAL BENEFITS: Reconfirms into your psyche how you choose to be – and this supercharging will carry over into your day!

MIND MANTRA:

"I am SUPERCHARGED with_____!"

(love, joy, peace, happiness, light, healing power, energy, gratitude…)

PHYSICAL BENEFITS: Exercises the vocal chords

DIRECTIONS: I like to do this one at the end of my walk. I just call out the mantra in a loud voice. Shout it out as many times as you want. Then for icing on the cake, follow it with the exercise "CLAP, CLAP, YAY, YAY!" or just a great big "YES!"

TAKE A BOW

SPIRITUAL BENEFITS: Humility, Gratitude

MIND MANTRA:
On my knees
I humbly bow
Nothing can compare
To Thou

PHYSICAL BENEFITS: Muscular relaxation

DIRECTIONS: Out on the grass or on Mother Earth somewhere, simply kneel and bring your forehead down to touch the ground. Arms may be stretched overhead or down to your sides. Repeat mantra and remain in silence for a few minutes.

TARZAN CALL

SPIRITUAL BENEFIT: Courage, Strength

MIND MANTRA:

Awwwwe!

Me Strong and Courageous!

PHYSICAL BENEFITS: Stimulates heart and helps to clear and open the lungs. Relaxes tension and anxiety

DIRECTIONS: Standing tall and proud, alternately thump chest with your fists, like Tarzan. Take a deep inhalation, relax jaw and sound out a long strong "Awwwwe."

Then, with arms out to the side, elbows bent to 90 degrees and hands still in fisted position, repeat with a strong affirmative voice: "Me strong and courageous!" Return fists to the chest, thumping. Repeat several times.

"The bravest thing you can do when you are not brave is to profess courage and act accordingly."

– Corra Harris

THE BEE

(a walking meditation)

SPIRITUAL BENEFITS: Sweetness, Compassion

MIND MANTRA:

Like a bee, I hum along

Softly will I sing my song

Oh the nectar is so sweet

It is God in all I meet

PHYSICAL BENEFITS: Massages the vocal cords, warms your voice

DIRECTIONS: Begin humming. Hum, hum and hum. In between the humming, sing the mantra in whatever little melody that comes out. Go back and forth from humming to singing.

"God must become an activity in our consciousness."
— Joel S. Goldsmith

THE BELLA WAGGLE

SPIRITUAL BENEFITS: Happiness, Lightness

MIND MANTRA:

I am so happy

So very happy

I am as happy as can be

When I wag more

And I bark less

I feel happy and

Not so stressed!

(I sometimes sing it to the tune of "You Are My Sunshine.")

PHYSICAL BENEFITS: Increases circulation into abdominal and buttocks area. Exercises breath control

DIRECTIONS: Standing with knees softly bent and buttocks slightly sticking out behind you, place your hands in front of your chest like two little paws. With your tongue hanging out of your mouth begin panting fast and shallow like a dog. At the same time wag a pretend tail behind you as fast and excitedly as you can. Alternate between saying the mantra out loud and then silently repeating it as you pant. You might try it when a good friend that you're excited to see comes to your door. I named this exercise after my late beloved dog, Bella. She was always so happy and excited about the simplest things in life – like whenever I came home. Her tail would wag so hard that it would practically knock her off her paws. Bella means "beautiful" in Italian. The Beautiful Waggle! Embrace your beautiful waggle! (p.s. DOG spelled backwards: GOD!)

THE BIRD CALL

SPIRITUAL BENEFIT: Freedom of Expression, Empowerment to Create, Courage to Request

MIND MANTRA:

Ka-Kaaaaaaa, Ka-Kaaaaaaaa

(Translation: I call forth_____ in my life. Fill in the blank with your deepest wishes and dreams.)

PHYSICAL BENEFITS: Exercises vocal cords, Strengthens diaphragm

DIRECTIONS: I have a special spot at a cliff edge overlooking the ocean where I enjoy doing this.

I really love to do it on a windy day because the wind carries my request into the universe. But any day, anywhere, in whatever weather condition is just fine. (I actually envision doing it on a busy city corner, like in NY or LA someday! Maybe with a small flock of like-feathered friends!)

Setting an intention, a dream, a desire or a request in my mind, I attach it to the sound of my bird call. As loud, strong and determined as I can, I cry out "Ka-Kaaaaaa." I repeat it many times and make as many requests and bird calls as I want. I continue until I feel satisfied and know the Universe has heard me. Afterward, I pause and close my eyes. I smile. I *know* my requests are being answered.

THE BOAT

SPIRITUAL BENEFITS: Strength, Endurance, Persistence, Direction

MIND MANTRA:

Like a boat

Out on the sea

I navigate

To follow Thee

PHYSICAL BENEFITS: Strengthens the back muscles and stimulates the kidney meridian

DIRECTIONS: Lie on stomach, legs close together and arms by sides. Lift legs, shoulders, arms, chest and head while arching your back and looking forward, like a boat. Repeat the mantra while sustaining the position and then relax back into starting position. Repeat five times.

THE BRIDGE

SPIRITUAL BENEFITS: Recognition of our connection to Spirit

MIND MANTRA:

I am a bridge for_____

(Peace, Love, Joy, Happiness, etc.)

PHYSICAL BENEFITS: Strengthens buttocks, hamstring and low back muscles

DIRECTIONS: Lying on back with knees bent and feet placed hip-width apart close to buttocks, lift the buttocks up into the air. Strongly squeeze your muscles as you repeat the mantra.

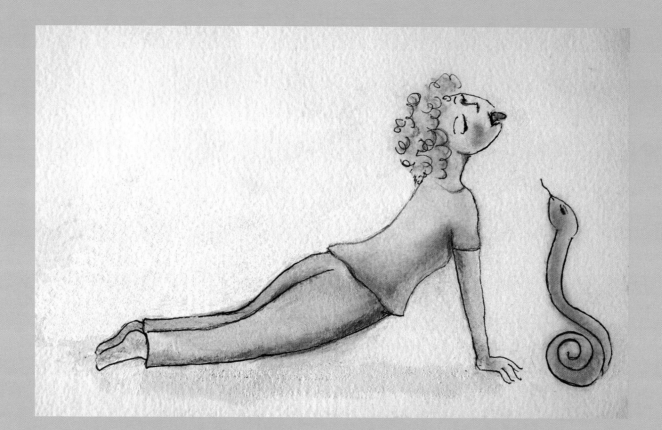

THE COBRA MOUTHWASH

SPIRITUAL BENEFIT: Purification. Releases anxiety

MIND MANTRA:

I stick out my tongue and say, "Ahhhhhh. . ."

As I let in the Sun to clean and do its thing

Gargle, swish and spit

I clean my mouth out

PHYSICAL BENEFITS: Great for the low back as well as releasing tension in the throat and jaw

DIRECTIONS: Lying on your stomach with legs together, bend your elbows and place your hands underneath your shoulders. Keeping your hips on the floor, slowly straighten elbows, arching your back as far as you can. Once you are as high as you can go, take a big breath in. Relax your low back and buttocks muscles as you let your breath out. Now, for the mouthwash. Open your jaw nice and wide and stick your tongue out as far as you can. As you take another big breath, exhale and vocalize a big, long, "Ahhhhhh". Let the Sun shine down upon your tongue, inside your mouth and throat. Imagine that it is cleaning away any old verbal garbage that your tongue may have a habit of engaging in. Once the Sun has loosened it all up, gargle, swish (side to side and all around), and then spit (a pretend one) it out!

THE GLIDER

SPIRITUAL BENEFITS: Perspective, Focus, Balance

MIND MANTRA:

Like a glider in the sky

I *am* focused and balanced

And/Or:

All my problems

Down below,

Have become quite small

You know!

PHYSICAL BENEFITS: Improves balance, stretches and strengthens legs, arms and trunk.

DIRECTIONS: Stand with one foot firmly on ground. Slowly bend your body horizontally as you lift hands out to side and one leg out behind you. Try to get as strong, straight and horizontal to the ground as you can as you balance on one leg. Repeat on the other side. Repeat mantra slowly as you stay focused. Become an inner observer with a grand perspective.

THE HUG

SPIRITUAL BENEFITS: Self-Love, Appreciation and Gratitude

(I tell my kids hugs are important – like drinking water, we need at least eight of them a day. Now that they are all grown and gone, I sometimes find myself without so many hugs. So, I have learned to just give myself my own hugs! They're important ones to give!)

MIND MANTRA:

I hug myself so big

I hug myself so long

I'm just so darn delicious

I might just sing myself a song!

PHYSICAL BENEFITS: Stretches your upper back muscles. Research says it takes a 20-second hug to release oxytocin, the bonding hormone that allows you to establish a deep connection with others — and, of course, yourself, too! Oxytocin also reduces your blood pressure. So hug and be hugged! Love and be loved!

DIRECTIONS: Simply cross your arms around the front of your chest, hands to opposite shoulders and give yourself a big, long hug! Let your hug last for a good, long 20 seconds. Repeat your mind mantra. (The "LA-LA-LA" or "Sing Your Name" exercises are a nice follow-up for this.)

THE LIGHTHOUSE

SPIRITUAL BENEFITS: Praying, sharing and blessing others with love

MIND MANTRA:

Like a lighthouse

I will call,

"OOOOOOMMMMMMMM"

Sending love

To one and all

Like a lighthouse

I will shine

Silent beams

Of light divine

PHYSICAL BENEFITS: Stretches shoulders and trunk. Strengthens core and extremities

DIRECTIONS: Standing with arms stretched overhead, send and feel the energy down into your arms, fingertips, chest, buttocks and legs. Contract all your muscles. Repeat the mantra. After every repetition of the mantra, turn a little so you eventually make a full circle, sending your love out to friends, family, neighborhood, community, island, nation and world.

THE MOUNTAIN

SPIRITUAL BENEFIT: Calmness and Strength

MIND MANTRA:

Like a mountain

I am strong

Like Haleakala

I am calm

I stay grounded

All day long

PHYSICAL BENEFITS: Stretches hamstrings, calves, heel-cords, shoulders and back. Increases circulation to your head and brain. Reverses the effects of gravity on your face

DIRECTIONS: With feet on the ground, hip-width apart, place hands on the ground shoulder-width apart. Push hips up into air so that you form an upside-down "V" position. Try to keep knees straight and heels flat on the ground. Feel the stretch down the back of your thighs and calves. This position is often called "Down-Dog." Repeat mantra. Let your head be relaxed as it hangs upside down.

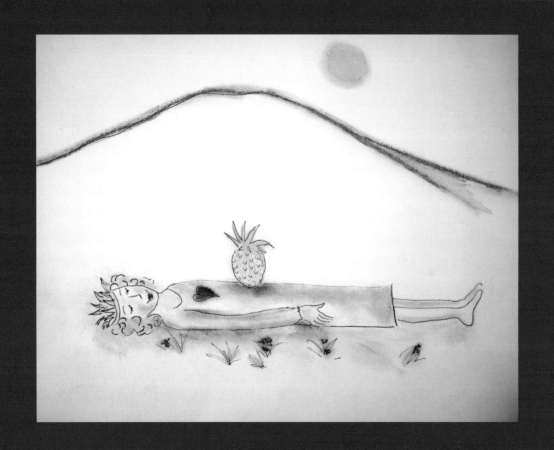

THE PINEAPPLE GLOW

(a lying meditation)

SPIRITUAL BENEFIT: A Golden Glowing Radiance

MIND MANTRA:

I am filled with a golden glow
And right now, this is all I need to know

PHYSICAL BENEFIT: Relaxation

DIRECTIONS: Lying comfortably on your back, place a pineapple on your chest or stomach. (Laying it on its side makes it easier to balance.)

Close your eyes and begin to breathe deeply as you visualize a golden glow entering your body with every breath. See the golden light from the pineapple filling up every part of your body. Breathe in deeply until you feel completely relaxed and beautiful. You will be glowing with sweet, golden light all day!

(And remember, if ever you are wearing a frown, put on your "pineapple crown"!
YOU ARE ROYALTY!)

THE POOPER!

SPIRITUAL BENEFITS: Letting go of unwanted "poop" in your life. Doubts, fears, regrets, feelings of being not good enough, not deserving enough, remorse, depression, anger, etc.

MIND MANTRA:

I release and I let go

All my poop of any kind

Even from a past lifetime

I release and I let go

Into the compost bin it flows

PHYSICAL BENEFITS: Stretches hip, thigh and calf muscles

DIRECTIONS: While squatting, hands in prayer position with elbows pressing out against inner side of knees, repeat the mantra. Afterward, place your hands on your heart and feel happy and thankful that you are acknowledging poop and letting it go!

THE PRAYER WALK

SPIRITUAL BENEFITS: Focus, connection, gratitude, trust. There seems to me to be a certain "magic" in placing your hands in prayer position. It feels like it brings a balance or connection of the two brain hemispheres and it seems to just tickle the pineal gland (the "third eye"). If the pineal gland can go from dry and shriveled to sweet and juicy, this is one exercise that will do it!

MIND MANTRA:

Thank you for the love divine
Thank for the light that shines
Thank you for this life of mine

PHYSICAL BENEFITS: All that comes with walking

DIRECTIONS: Walk slowly with your hands in prayer position.

"Love is not something you produce; love is not something you have; love is something that has you."

— Anthony de Mello

THIGHS ALIVE

SPIRITUAL BENEFITS: Gratitude, Humility

MIND MANTRA:
I stretch my thighs
And feel alive
And bow to the One
Who fuels the sun!

PHYSICAL BENEFITS: Stretches inner thigh muscles. Lubricates hip joints

DIRECTIONS: Sitting with your knees flexed and soles of feet together, hold your feet with your hands.

Slowly bend your body forward, as if to bow, while you repeat the mantra. Slowly go back and forth, feeling the stretch in your inner thigh muscles. Hold the position for a longer stretch as you repeat the mantra, contemplate and thank the One who fuels the sun.

TIGHTROPE WALK

SPIRITUAL BENEFIT: Steadiness, Focus of Mind

MENTAL MANTRA:

Sublime and calm

I walk the line

I decipher delusion

And stay away from confusion

This way I know

Will lead me home!

Or

Teach me, guide me

Balance my way

I love you sweet Spirit

Within me today

PHYSICAL BENEFIT: Balance and coordination

DIRECTIONS: Walk slowly, as on a tightrope, with arms out to side to help balance. Point and slightly lift and straighten front leg before placing it down in front of you. Place one front foot directly in front of the other. To increase difficulty, slowly lift arms out to the side and move them up and down alternately. To increase difficulty even more, rotate head from side to side while looking at the hand that is coming down.

TRUST WE MUST

SPIRITUAL BENEFITS: Building Trust in Spirit

MIND MANTRA

Trust, trust, trust I must

In the Divine, I trust, trust, trust!

PHYSICAL BENEFITS: Strengthens the gluteus muscles

DIRECTIONS: Your gluteus, or buttocks muscles, are what I call your "Trust" muscles. Every time you work them out, such as when doing this exercise or when hiking uphill, tell yourself that you are building up trust! I have strong fit "Trust" muscles!

Go for a little burn in that muscle to ensure you are accumulating a good storage of trust! When we fill this very large muscle group with trust, we will surely have a surplus when challenges arise. Holding onto a tree stump, a rock, a gate or anything stable that is about waist high, form the letter "T". Do this by placing both outstretched arms on the tree stump and making a horizontal line (top of the "T") with one leg outstretched horizontally behind you. Your standing leg is the vertical line of the "T". Begin by tightly squeezing your buttocks muscle of the leg that is in the air. Make a very strong, straight horizontal leg. See how strong you can make it. Then begin making small pumping movements or contractions, slightly lifting the horizontal leg up and down. Repeat up to 20 times while you are saying the mantra and pressing "trust" into your buttocks muscle. Continue to work that muscle by doing up to ten kicks into the air with that same leg. Do this by bending the knee into the chest and then straightening and kicking the leg out behind you.

(Some call this the Donkey Kick.) Feel like you are pushing any doubt and weakness out of your body. Now, bring that same leg over to the side and, with knee bent, begin doing small circles, ten clockwise, ten counterclockwise. (Some call this the Doggie/Fire-Hydrant Exercise.) By the end of the sequence you should feel a little 'burn' in the muscle. Shake it out and then repeat on the other side. Be sure to remember to listen to your body and do what challenges you just enough, and in this way you can slowly build up your "trust" account!

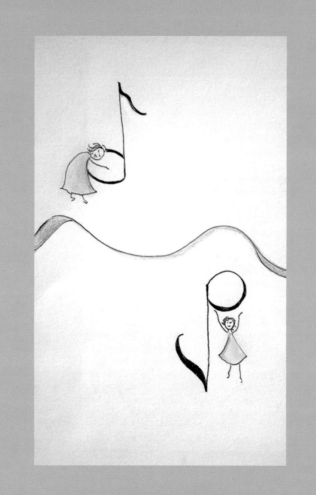

TUNE UP TIME!

SPIRITUAL BENEFITS: Discrimination, Power of Choice, Assertiveness

MIND MANTRA:

I tune myself

With Divine Harmony

I tune myself

With the Will of God

I tune myself with Love

(or Joy, Peace, Thankfulness, etc. Add any quality that you desire.)

PHYSICAL BENEFITS: Improves listening. Warms vocal cords

DIRECTIONS: Sing one note that is comfortable in your range, like "oooooh." Sing the whole mantra on that same note. Repeat, changing to a new pitch.

"I played the Vina until my heart turned into this very instrument; then I offered this instrument to the divine musician, the only musician existing. Since then I have become His flute; and when he chooses, He plays his music. The people give me credit for this music, which is in reality not due to me but to the musician who plays his own instrument."

— Hazrat Inayat Khan

UPSIDE DOWN

SPIRITUAL BENEFIT: Gaining broader perspective, Releasing attachments

MIND MANTRA:

Hangin' upside down

I shake out the clutter of my mind

More room for happiness

Is what I find!

PHYSICAL BENEFITS: Stretches hamstrings and inner thigh muscles, increases blood flow to face and head. Reverses effects of gravity on the face. Allows neck a little traction as it hangs

DIRECTIONS: Standing with your legs wide apart, bend forward and just let your head loosely hang upside down. Pretend that you have opened the lid of your mind and gently shake your head as you dump out all the useless thoughts you are storing in your brain. Stay there until they all drain out. Release the tension in your body as well as in your mind. Do this every day. Repeat the mantra.

V FOR VICTORY!

SPIRITUAL BENEFITS: Spiritual victory

MIND MANTRA:

V is for Victory!

Rah Rah Rah

Life is a precious mystery

Sis Boom Bah!

PHYSICAL BENEFITS: Stretches and strengthens inner thigh muscles

DIRECTIONS: Lying on your back, bring your legs straight into the air above you.

Spread them out into a "V" position and say the mantra. Bring them back and forth, together and then apart, finishing with one longer stretch.

"The hardest work of all is to do nothing."
    – Jewish saying

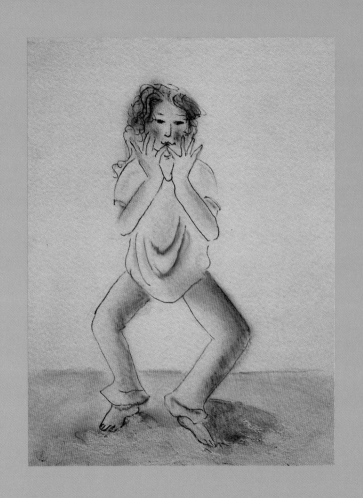

YOU'RE GROUNDED!

SPIRIT BENEFITS: Grounding, Strength, Beauty, Simplicity, Common Sense, Earthiness, Self-Acceptance.

MIND MANTRA:

As a seed I am nourished below
As a beautiful flower I blossom and grow

PHYSICAL BENEFITS: Stretches thighs and hips

DIRECTIONS: In a wide squatting position on the ground (and barefoot whenever possible), place hands in prayer position in front of heart.

Repeat the first line of the mantra. You can stay in that position as you stretch and contemplate. Take several deep breaths and then bring your hands to an open flower position by keeping your baby fingers pressed together and your thumbs pressed together while your fingers open and spread apart, like a flower. As they do this, begin to slowly stand as your hands lift, separate and stretch toward the sky. Your arms will be stretched out in a "V" position as you come to an upright stance. Repeat the second line of the mantra. Return to squatting position and repeat several times.

Spiritual Category Index

Continued

Continued

GIVING AND SHARING

HUMILITY AND GRACE

LAUGHTER AND LIGHTNESS

Continued

PEACE AND STILLNESS

PURPOSE AND DETERMINATION

STRENGTH AND POWER

Continued

TRUST AND FAITH

VITALIZATION AND HEALING

HONGSAUYOGA.COM http://HONGSAUYOGA.COM

For purchase of:

Book

Private or semi-private Hong-Sau lessons

Retreats

Hong-Sau Yoga certification

Hong-Sau hats

Live exercise videos

My Evolution

Up until a year ago, June 2010, I worked in our western medical system as a physical therapist. Most of my years were spent in small private settings that allowed more freedom to combine a holistic and intuitive approach to healing. But from 2009 to 2010, I worked in a large, well-known HMO facility in the United States.

I wanted to work where I didn't have to do my own billing or office work, allowing me to focus only on my patients and treatment. Although Western medicine has made great strides and advocates many preventive measures, it continues to focus on symptoms and the majority of treatment is with pharmaceuticals. Because they have been taught with a left-brain approach to looking at medicine, it is very foreign for most Western medical personnel to incorporate a holistic, intuitive approach. I often think that they instinctively would like to, but the overriding big wheel that drives the machine instills fear and intimidation, and wants everyone to conform in a robotic, methodical way. Being true to how I view healing and healthful living, I no longer work there and have decided to spend my time and effort promoting well-being that starts from within. Don't get me wrong, I still love fitness and exercise, and our health facilities have a lot to offer. The difference lies in where we put our focus and priority, and is about having balance in our lives. Our mortal bodies will grow old, but it's "the twinkle in the eye, not the wrinkle in the thigh" that matters most!

Addressing our spiritual nature does not have to be equated to religion or "pushing" one's beliefs onto another. Give Spirit any name you are comfortable with, but scientifically see Spirit as the omnipresent, omnipotent, intelligent driving force and wisdom behind all we see and don't see in our material world.

As we make the choice every day to open and follow our hearts and focus our attention on the Divine, our lives and our world begin to heal and flourish. Choose to align yourself with that supreme consciousness today!